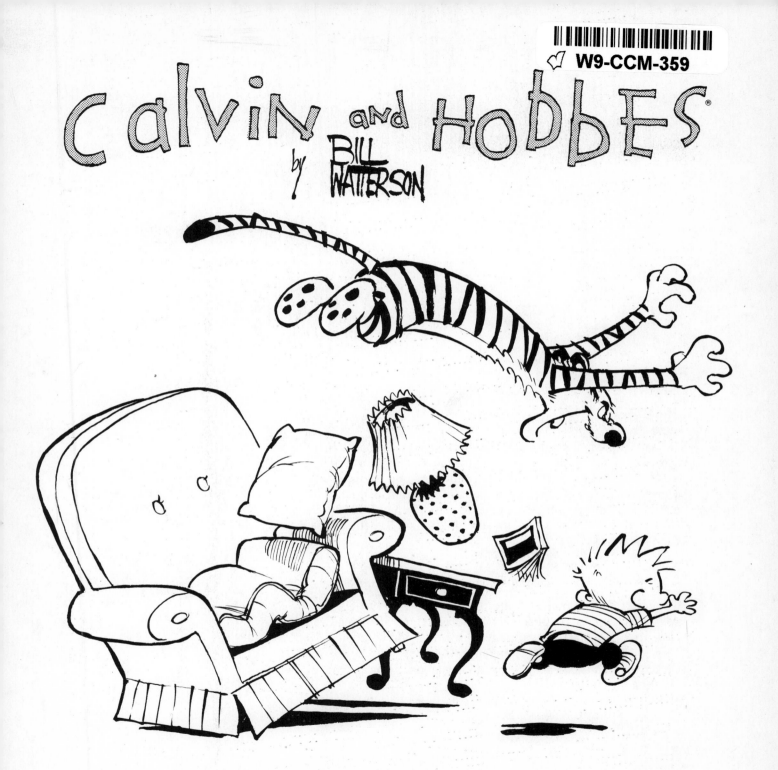

Calvin and Hobbes

by Bill Watterson

SCHOLASTIC INC.

New York Toronto London Auckland Sydney
Mexico City New Delhi Hong Kong

ISBN-13: 978-0-590-06756-0
ISBN-10: 0-590-06756-7

36 35 34 33 32   7 8 9 / 0

Printed in the U.S.A.

Foreword

There are few wellsprings of humor more consistently reliable than the mind of a child. Most cartoonists, being childlike, recognize this, but when they set out to capture the hurly-burly of the very young, they almost always cheat, shamelessly creating not recognizable children, but highly annoying, wisecracking, miniature adults. Chalk it up to either indolence or defective recall, but most people who write comic dialogue for minors (up to and including the perpetrators of the Cosby "kids") demonstrate surprisingly little feel for — or faith in — the original source material, that is, childhood, in all its unfettered and winsome glory.

It is in this respect that Bill Watterson has proved as unusual as his feckless creations, Calvin and Hobbes. Watterson is the reporter who's gotten it right; childhood as it actually *is*, with its constantly shifting frames of reference. Anyone who's done time with a small child knows that reality can be highly situational. The utterance which an adult knows to be a "lie" may well reflect a child's deepest conviction, at least at the moment it pops out. Fantasy is so accessible, and it is joined with such force and frequency, that resentful parents like Calvin's assume they are being manipulated, when the truth is far more frightening: they don't even exist. The child is both king and keeper of this realm, and he can be very choosey about the company he keeps.

Of course, this exclusivity only provokes many grown-ups into trying to regain the serendipity of youth for themselves, to, in effect, retrieve the irretrievable. A desperate few do things that later land them in the Betty Ford Center.

The rest of us, more sensibly, read Calvin and Hobbes.

— GARRY TRUDEAU

OUTRAGE! WHY SHOULD I GO TO BED? I'M NOT TIRED! IT'S ONLY 7:30! THIS IS TYRANNY! I'M!

8

ANY MONSTERS UNDER MY BED TONIGHT?!

NOPE!

NO!

UH-UH.

WELL, THERE'D BETTER **NOT** BE! I'D HATE TO HAVE TO **TORCH** ONE WITH MY FLAME THROWER!

YOU HAVE A FLAME THROWER??

THEY LIE. I LIE.

MOM, CAN I DRIVE ON THE WAY BACK?

OF COURSE NOT, CALVIN.

CAN I JUST STEER THEN? I PROMISE I WON'T CRASH.

NO, CALVIN.

CAN I WORK THE GAS AND BRAKES WHILE **YOU** STEER?

NO, CALVIN.

YOU NEVER LET ME DO ANYTHING.

HERE WE FIND A THRIVING CITY: BRAND NEW BUILDINGS, A BUSTLING ECONOMY.

A SCENIC THOROUGHFARE WINDS THROUGH THIS HAPPY MUNICIPALITY. HERE, A FARMER DRIVES HIS LIVESTOCK TO MARKET.

TRAGICALLY, THIS SERENE METROPOLIS LIES DIRECTLY BENEATH THE HOOVER DAM...

9

BAD NEWS, DAD. YOUR POLLS ARE WAY DOWN.

MY POLLS?

YOU RATE ESPECIALLY LOW AMONG TIGERS AND SIX-YEAR-OLD WHITE MALES.

IF YOU WANT TO STAY "DAD," I'D SUGGEST YOU ADOPT SOME KEY PLANKS TO YOUR PLATFORM.

SOME SPECIAL INTEREST GROUPS ARE IN FOR A SURPRISE.

OF THOSE POLLED, VIRTUALLY ALL FAVOR INCREASED ALLOWANCES AND THE COMMENCEMENT OF DRIVING LESSONS.

THERE'S A NEW GIRL IN OUR CLASS.

WELL! WHAT'S HER NAME?

WHO KNOWS?

IS SHE NICE?

WHO CARES? NOT ME!

DO YOU *LIKE* HER??

NO!

HERE COMES THAT NEW GIRL.

HEY SUSIE DERKINS, IS THAT YOUR FACE, OR IS A 'POSSUM STUCK IN YOUR COLLAR?

I HOPE YOU SUFFER A DEBILITATING BRAIN ANEURYSM, YOU FREAK!

SHE'S *CUTE*, ISN'T SHE??

GO AWAY.

OUR HERO, THE VALIANT SPACEMAN SPIFF, IS MAROONED ON A STRANGE WORLD...

I'LL SET MY MERTILIZER ON "DEEP FAT FRY."

CALVIN! YOU'RE NOT PAYING ATTENTION!

..WE JOIN SPACEMAN SPIFF ON THE DISTANT PLANET ZORG...

GRONK! ARGH!

ZOUNDS!

TRAPPED BY A HIDEOUS GRAKNIL, SPIFF DRAWS HIS TRUSTY ATOMIC NAPALM NEUTRALIZER!

CHEW ELECTRIC DEATH, SNARLING CUR!

BUT THE WEAPON IS USELESS! SPIFF IS DOOMED!!

OUR HERO MAKES A BREAK, AND DUCKS INTO A NEARBY CAVE!

WEEOOO! WHAT'S THAT AWFUL SMELL?

EEP!

TEACHERS LOUNGE

WHO WAS THAT?

BEATS ME, FRED.

SLAM!

WATTERSON

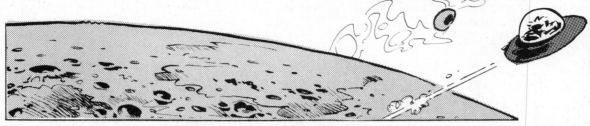

DIG DIG

PAT PAT

CALVIN! WHAT ARE YOU DOING TO OUR YARD?!?

MAKING SPEED BUMPS.

I WONDER WHERE WE GO WHEN WE DIE.

PITTSBURGH?

YOU MEAN IF WE'RE GOOD OR IF WE'RE BAD?

WE'RE LOST AGAIN.

HA! WE'RE BRAVE EXPLORERS!

THE WORD "LOST" ISN'T EVEN IN OUR VOCABULARY!

HOW ABOUT THE WORD "MOMMY"?

MOMMMYYY!!

HEY! WHERE'S THE STOCKING FOR HOBBES?

WHERE'S SANTA GONNA STICK HOBBES' LOOT, IF HOBBES DOESN'T HAVE A STOCKING?!?

OKAY, OKAY... I'LL MAKE HOBBES A STOCKING, DON'T WORRY.

MAKE IT BIG, BUT NOT AS BIG AS MINE.

"HOBBES' LOOT"??

DON'T LOOK AT ME! I'M DONE SHOPPING!

ARE YOU STILL AWAKE?

OF COURSE!

IT'S MIDNIGHT. LET'S GO!

AS SOON AS HE DROPS THE BAG DOWN, YOU GRAB IT, AND I'LL CLOSE THE FLUE!

UH, HOBBES?... I FORGOT TO GET YOU A PRESENT. I DIDN'T EVEN MAKE YOU A CARD...

I'M SORRY, HOBBES. I DIDN'T MEAN TO FORGET.

IT'S OKAY, LITTLE BUDDY. I DIDN'T GET YOU ANYTHING EITHER.

BUT HERE'S A TIGER HUG FOR BEING MY BEST FRIEND.

NOT SO HARD, YOU BIG SISSY. YOU SQUEEZE MY TEARS OUT.

MERRY CHRISTMAS.

22

24

ALL RIGHT, CLASS, WHO WOULD LIKE TO GIVE HIS BOOK REPORT FIRST?

CALVIN, HOW ABOUT YOU?

CALVIN?

CALVIN? SPACEMAN SPIFF COOLY DRAWS HIS DEATH RAY BLASTER...

$2 + 7 = \underline{\quad}$

I cannot answer this qwestion, as it is against my religious principles.

IT'S WORTH A SHOT.

HOBBES, WHAT DO YOU THINK HAPPENS TO US WHEN WE DIE?

I THINK WE PLAY SAXOPHONE FOR AN ALL-GIRL CABARET IN NEW ORLEANS.

SO YOU BELIEVE IN HEAVEN?

CALL IT WHAT YOU LIKE.

28

I'M HOME FROM SCHOOL!

SO I GATHERED.

HOBBES?

YAAAAAH!

AAAAUGH! TIGER ATTACK!

GRRRR RRRRRRRR RRRRRRR

BINK BONK BANG BOING

CALVIN! QUIT CRASHING AROUND!

HOBBES JUMPED ME, MOM! I WAS FIGHTING FOR MY VERY SURVIVAL!!

SURE, CALVIN. LOOK, I DON'T WANT TO SEW HOBBES UP AGAIN, SO WHY DON'T YOU TWO GO DO SOMETHING QUIET?

OKAY, OKAY...

YOU SISSY. MOM ALWAYS TAKES YOUR SIDE!

THAT'S BECAUSE SHE WANTED ANOTHER TIGER, NOT YOU!

30

33

DO YOU KNOW WHERE BABIES COME FROM?

NOPE.

WELL, I WONDER HOW ONE FINDS OUT!

...HERE, LET ME SEE THE BACK OF YOUR SHIRT.

YOU CAME FROM TAIWAN.

HEY, MOM, WHEN'S LUNCH?

LATER, CALVIN. I'M BUSY.

BUT I'M HUNGRY NOW! I WANNA EAT!

A MAP TO THE REFRIGERATOR. HILARIOUS.

HI, DAD. IT'S ME, CALVIN!

HOW'S WORK GOING? ...UH HUH... PRETTY DAY OUT, ISN'T IT? ...YEP.....

ARE YOU BRINGING ME HOME ANY PRESENTS TONIGHT? ...NO? WELL, JUST THOUGHT I'D ASK...

LISTEN, I SUPPOSE YOU'RE WONDERING WHY I CALLED...

DAD, YOUR POLLS TOOK A BIG DIVE THIS WEEK.

YOUR "OVERALL DAD PERFORMANCE" RATING WAS ESPECIALLY LOW.

SEE? RIGHT ABOUT YESTERDAY YOUR POPULARITY WENT DOWN THE TUBES.

CALVIN, YOU DIDN'T GET DESSERT YESTERDAY BECAUSE YOU FLOODED THE HOUSE!!

I'D SUGGEST A NEW LINE OF WORK, "DAD"...

THE GIANT SLIMY OCTOPUS OOZES ACROSS THE BEACH.

HIS HIDEOUS PRESENCE TERRORIZES THE SLEEPY WATERFRONT COMMUNITY.

WITH A SUCKER-COVERED TENTACLE, HE GRABS AN UNSUSPECTING TOURIST.

A MUFFLED SCREAM LINGERS IN THE SALTY AIR!

DID YOU WANT SOMETHING, CALVIN?

ACK ICK IG

UH-OH, HERE COMES MOE, THE CLASS BULLY!

Okay twinky, let's have that ball.

SURE, MOE. ALL YOURS

NEVER ARGUE WITH A SIX-YEAR-OLD WHO SHAVES.

Hey! You took my favorite swing!

THAT'S TRUE, MOE. HOW ABOUT THAT?

..uh..

HIS TRAIN OF THOUGHT IS STILL BOARDING AT THE STATION.

MOE, I WAS WONDERING SOMETHING.

ARE YOUR MALADJUSTED ANTISOCIAL TENDENCIES THE PRODUCT OF YOUR BERSERK PITUITARY GLAND?

what?

ISN'T HE GREAT, FOLKS? LET'S GIVE HIM A BIG HAND!

WHAT SHOULD WE HAVE DAD READ US TONIGHT?

..SO IN THE NEXT PANEL, SUPERTOAD GOES "PLOOIE", AND...

"'MY, WHAT BIG TEETH YOU HAVE!' SAID LITTLE RED RIDING HOOD. 'THE BETTER TO EAT YOU WITH!' SAID THE WOLF..."

TIGER.

"...SAID THE TIGER, AND HE POUNCED ON LITTLE RED RIDING HOOD."

"JUST THEN A HUNTER CAME BY, AND WHEN HE SAW THE WOLF..."

TIGER.

"..WHEN HE SAW THE TIGER, HE PICKED UP HIS GUN AND..."

..AND?

"..AND IT WAS TOO LATE. THE TIGER ATE THEM BOTH AND HE LIVED HAPPILY EVER AFTER. THE END."

GOOD STORY, DAD! THANKS!

SNIFF I ALWAYS CRY AT HAPPY ENDINGS.

"A BUSHEL IS A UNIT OF WEIGHT EQUAL TO FOUR PECKS."

WHAT'S A PECK?

A QUICK SMOOCH.

YOU KNOW, I DON'T UNDERSTAND MATH AT ALL.

MOM, CAN I HAVE SOME MONEY SO HOBBES AND I CAN GO TO A MOVIE?

WHAT MOVIE?

"THE CUISINART MURDERER OF CENTRAL HIGH."

I REALLY THINK THERE ARE MORE CONSTRUCTIVE WAYS YOU COULD SPEND YOUR AFTERNOON, CALVIN.

WHAT DID SHE SAY?

OH, SHE WENT OFF ON ONE OF HER IRRELEVANT TANGENTS AGAIN.

DO YOU BELIEVE OUR DESTINIES ARE CONTROLLED BY THE STARS?

NO, I THINK WE CAN DO WHATEVER WE WANT WITH OUR LIVES.

NOT TO HEAR MOM AND DAD TELL IT.

WAKE UP, CALVIN. IT'S TIME FOR SCHOOL.

I'M NOT GOING TO SCHOOL ANYMORE.

YOU HAVE TO. IT'S THE LAW.

WHAT ABOUT HOBBES? WHY DOESN'T *HE* HAVE TO GO TO SCHOOL?

HE'S A TIGER. GET UP.

WHAT'S BEING A TIGER GOT TO DO WITH IT?

TIGERS WRECK THE GRADE CURVE.

DO YOU THINK IT'S BETTER TO LIVE IN STUPEFYING SECURITY...

...OR TO TAKE RISKS AND LIVE LIFE ON THE EDGE?

I THINK IT'S BETTER TO ACCEPT DANGER AND LIVE TO THE FULLEST!

I TAKE IT BY YOUR SILENCE THAT YOU AGREE...

I'M MAKING SUSIE DERKINS A VALENTINE.

SHE'S A CUTIE, ALL RIGHT.

SEE, I MADE A BIG RED HEART.

NOW I'M PUTTING LACE AROUND IT.

THAT'S VERY SWEET. I'M SURE SHE'LL LIKE IT.

Susie,
I hate you. Drop dead.
Calvin

I'D LIKE TO GET A VALENTINE BOUQUET FOR A GIRL I KNOW.

WHAT A SWEET LITTLE BOY YOU ARE! COME SEE WHAT WE HAVE.

IS THIS ALL?

DID YOU HAVE SOMETHING SPECIAL IN MIND?

SORT OF. DO YOU HAVE A DUMPSTER OUT BACK I COULD ROOT THROUGH?

CALVIN, YOU BALONEY BRAIN!

YOU SENT ME A HATE-MAIL VALENTINE AND A CRUMMY BUNCH OF DEAD FLOWERS!

SO HERE'S A VALENTINE FOR *YOU*, YOU INSENSITIVE CLOD!!

POW

A VALENTINE AND FLOWERS! HE *LIKES* ME!

SHE NOTICED! SHE *LIKES* ME!

45

HEY, CALVIN! ARE WE NEAR A SLAUGHTERHOUSE, OR DID YOU FORGET YOUR DEODORANT?!

DROP DEAD, SUSIE! YOU'RE SO UGLY, I HEAR YOUR MOM PUTS A BAG OVER YOUR HEAD BEFORE SHE KISSES YOU GOODNIGHT!!

IT'S SHAMELESS THE WAY WE FLIRT.

WHAT'S IT LIKE TO FALL IN LOVE?

WELL... SAY THE OBJECT OF YOUR AFFECTION WALKS BY...

YEAH?

FIRST, YOUR HEART FALLS INTO YOUR STOMACH AND SPLASHES YOUR INNARDS.

ALL THE MOISTURE MAKES YOU SWEAT PROFUSELY.

THIS CONDENSATION SHORTS THE CIRCUITS TO YOUR BRAIN, AND YOU GET ALL WOOZY.

WHEN YOUR BRAIN BURNS OUT ALTOGETHER, YOUR MOUTH DISENGAGES AND YOU BABBLE LIKE A CRETIN UNTIL SHE LEAVES.

THAT'S LOVE?!?

MEDICALLY SPEAKING.

HECK, THAT HAPPENED TO ME ONCE, BUT I FIGURED IT WAS COOTIES!!

WATTERSON

Hey, Calvin, it's gonna cost you 50 cents to be my friend today.

AND WHAT IF I DON'T *WANT* TO BE YOUR FRIEND TODAY?

Then the janitor scrapes you off the wall with a spatula.

HECK, WHAT'S A LITTLE EXTORTION AMONG FRIENDS?

I GOT THE NEW ALBUM BY SCRAMBLED DEBUTANTE.

ALL THEIR SONGS GLORIFY DEPRAVED VIOLENCE, MINDLESS SEX, AND THE DELIBERATE ABUSE OF DANGEROUS DRUGS.

YOUR MOM'S GOING TO GO INTO CONNIPTIONS WHEN SHE SEES *THIS* LYING AROUND.

WELL I SURE DIDN'T BUY IT FOR THE MUSIC..

MOM, WILL YOU DRIVE ME INTO TOWN?

WHY SHOULD I *DRIVE* YOU, CALVIN? IT'S A PERFECT DAY OUTSIDE!

WHAT DO YOU THINK PEOPLE HAVE *FEET* FOR?

TO WORK THE GAS PEDAL.

47

CALVIN, YOU'RE NOT PAYING ATTENTION AGAIN!

SPACEMAN SPIFF, CONQUEROR OF THE COSMOS, IS TRAPPED BY A HIDEOUS ZONDARG!

WITH LIGHTNING SPEED, SPIFF BOLTS FOR THE AIR LOCK, MAKING A DARING ESCAPE!

NICE TRY, CALVIN.

I'M HOME!

DID YOU FEED HOBBES TODAY, MOM?

NO, DEAR, IT MUST HAVE SLIPPED MY MIND.

THANKS, MOM. YOU WANNA JUST DOUSE ME IN STEAK SAUCE BEFORE I GO TO MY ROOM?

MOMMMM!

I'M THIRSTY!

WHAT'S THIS? JUST WATER?

51

52

You're gonna taste asphalt fifth period, Twinky. Just so you know.

GREAT. I'M DEAD.

FIFTH PERIOD - "STUDIES IN CONTEMPORARY STATE-SPONSORED TERRORISM."

...ALSO KNOWN AS GYM CLASS.

I CAN'T GET A BABY SITTER ANYWHERE! WHAT SHOULD WE DO?

WE WON'T BE GONE LONG. COULDN'T CALVIN BE LEFT FOR A COUPLE HOURS UNSUPERVISED?

HA HA HA HA HA! HO HO HO HO HEE HE HA HOO HO HAR HA HO H

...SERIOUSLY... WHAT SHOULD WE DO?

HEE HEE

OKAY, CALVIN, WE'LL BE BACK IN A COUPLE OF HOURS.

YOU AND HOBBES JUST WATCH TV AND BE GOOD, OKAY?

DID YOU HEAR THAT? WE GET TO WATCH TV.!!

HOORAY!

VIDEORAMA? I'D LIKE TO RENT A VCR AND SOME MOVIES!

ASK IF THEY HAVE "ATTACK OF THE COED CANNIBALS."

HOW ARE YOU TODAY?

FINE.

I WANT THE TOP OF MY HEAD SHAVED, AND THE SIDES DYED PINK AND CUT IN HORIZONTAL STRIPES, OK?

MA'AM?

GIVE HIM THE USUAL, PETE.

WELL I GUESS THIS GUY KNOWS WHICH SIDE *HIS* BREAD IS BUTTERED ON!

THERE, HOW'S THAT LOOK?

THAT'S GREAT. PERFECT.

WITHOUT QUESTION, THIS IS THE FINEST HAIRCUT I HAVE EVER RECEIVED.

NEVER CRITICIZE A GUY WITH A RAZOR...

DO YOU LOVE ME, DAD?

OF COURSE I DO, CALVIN.

WOULD YOU STILL LOVE ME IF I DID SOMETHING BAD?

WELL OF COURSE ... I ... WOULD...

I MEAN SOMETHING REALLY *REALLY*..

CALVIN, WHAT DID YOU DO?!

WELL, DAD, YOUR POLLS ARE REAL HIGH THIS WEEK.

I'M GLAD TO HEAR THAT.

YEP, THOSE POLLED THINK YOU'RE DOING A FINE JOB AS DAD.

IN FACT, WITH A LITTLE PUSH TODAY, YOUR POLITICAL STOCK COULD REACH A RECORD HIGH.

NICE TRY. GO HELP YOUR MOM WITH THE DISHES.

OOH DAD! SUICIDE! OOH! OOH!

HERE COMES MOE, THE CLASS BULLY.

HE'S NOT SMART, BUT HE'S STREETWISE.

THAT MEANS HE KNOWS WHAT STREET HE LIVES ON.

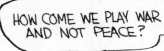

RISE AND SHINE, CALVIN!

MFGPBTHBBPT

THE EARLY BIRD GETS THE WORM!

BIG INCENTIVE.

I'VE DECIDED WE SHOULD BE "COOLER" THAN WE ARE.

WE'RE NOT COOL?

SURE WE'RE COOL. BUT WE'RE NOT AS COOL AS WE COULD BE.

COOL PEOPLE WEAR DARK GLASSES!

IT'S COOL TO BUMP INTO THINGS?

YOU DON'T MOVE, YOU JUST HANG AROUND.

HEY, DAD, WILL YOU BUY ME A FLAME THROWER?

OF COURSE NOT. DON'T BE SILLY.

EVEN IF I DIDN'T USE IT IN THE HOUSE?

I TOLD YOU I'M NOT SICK! WHAT'S THAT? WILL IT HURT?

IT'S A TONGUE DEPRESSOR. IT WON'T HURT AT ALL.

WHAT'S *THAT*? WILL IT HURT?

IT'S A STETHOSCOPE. IT WON'T HURT AT ALL.

WHAT'S *THAT*? WILL IT HURT?

IT'S A CATTLE PROD. IT HURTS A LITTLE LESS THAN A BRANDING IRON.

LITTLE KIDS HAVE NO SENSE OF HUMOR.

HEY, DOC, WHY ARE YOU RUBBING MY ARM WITH COTTON? ARE YOU GOING TO PUT A LEECH THERE?

ARE YOU GOING TO BLEED ME? YOU'RE NOT GOING TO AMPUTATE, ARE YOU? **ARE** YOU??

WHAT'S THAT? IS THAT A SHOT? ARE YOU GOING TO... **AAUGHH! IT WENT CLEAR THROUGH MY ARM!!** OW OW OW OW!!!

I'M DYING! PAID YOUR MALPRACTICE INSURANCE, YOU QUACK!! **WHERE'S MY MOM??!**

I HOPE YOU'VE

"SAFARI AL" HACKS HIS WAY THROUGH THE JUNGLE!

SUDDENLY, A GIANT GORILLA RIPS THROUGH THE FOLIAGE!

CLEAN YOUR ROOM.

WHAT?

YOU HEARD ME. IT'S A JUNGLE IN HERE!

SEEN ANY UFOs YET?

NOPE.

KEEP WATCHING THE MOON. ALIENS USUALLY TRY TO SNEAK UP FROM BEHIND IT.

WHAT ARE YOU DOING OUT HERE IN YOUR PAJAMAS? GET BACK IN BED!!

MOTHERS, ON THE OTHER HAND, SNEAK UP FROM BEHIND THE PACHYSANDRA PATCH.

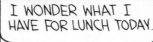
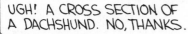

SOMEWHERE IN COMMUNIST RUSSIA I'LL BET THERE'S A LITTLE BOY WHO HAS NEVER KNOWN ANYTHING BUT **CENSORSHIP** AND **OPPRESSION**.

BUT MAYBE HE'S HEARD ABOUT **AMERICA**, AND HE DREAMS OF LIVING IN THIS LAND OF **FREEDOM** AND OPPORTUNITY!

SOMEDAY, I'D LIKE TO MEET THAT LITTLE BOY...

...AND TELL HIM THE AWFUL **TRUTH** ABOUT THIS PLACE!!

CALVIN, BE QUIET AND EAT THE STUPID LIMA BEANS.

WHENEVER I TAKE MY BATH...

...I ALWAYS PUT MY DUCKY IN FIRST.

FOR COMPANIONSHIP?

TO TEST FOR SHARKS.

MY SECRET ANCIENT TREASURE MAP SAYS TO DIG HERE!

LOOK! A WALLET FULL OF MONEY! RIGHT WHERE YOU SAID!

IT'S DAD'S. I BURIED IT HERE LAST WEEK.

SPACEMAN SPIFF, BOLD INTERPLANETARY EXPLORER, SPIES A ZARG!

SPIFF CALIBRATES HIS BLASTER. READY...AIM...

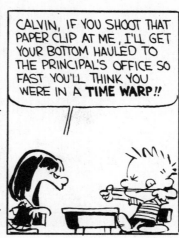

CALVIN, IF YOU SHOOT THAT PAPER CLIP AT ME, I'LL GET YOUR BOTTOM HAULED TO THE PRINCIPAL'S OFFICE SO FAST YOU'LL THINK YOU WERE IN A **TIME WARP**!!

CONFOUND IT. THE BLASTER JAMMED.

IT LOOKS LIKE HOBBES BURST A SEAM HERE. I'LL GET MY SEWING KIT.

IT'S JUST A LITTLE CUT. I DON'T NEED AN OPERATION. THIS IS UNNECESSARY SURGERY!

IT'S NOT SURGERY. YOU'RE JUST GETTING A COUPLE STITCHES! WHAT'S THE BIG DEAL?

YOUR MOM NEVER USES ANY ANESTHETIC.

WHAT A PECULIAR DREAM I HAD LAST NIGHT!

I DREAMED I WAS IN A BIG FIGHT WITH A FEROCIOUS WEASEL!

WHAT DO YOU SUPPOSE IT MEANS?

IT MEANS YOU'RE SLEEPING ON THE FLOOR TONIGHT, YOU NINCOMPOOP!

WHY SURE.

HEY DAD, REMEMBER OUR CAR?

WAIT A MINUTE. WHAT DO YOU MEAN, "REMEMBER"?

HOBBES, I HAVE A CONJECTURAL MORAL QUESTION. MAYBE YOU CAN HELP.

SURE.

SUPPOSE I DID SOMETHING BAD. SHOULD I TELL DAD?

HOW BAD ARE WE SUPPOSING?

WELL, HYPOTHETICALLY, LET'S SAY PRETTY BAD. LIKE TO HIS CAR, HYPOTHETICALLY.

HOW BAD, HYPOTHETICALLY, TO HIS CAR?

WELL, LET'S PRETEND IT WAS *REAL* BAD.

SHOULD WE PRETEND IT COULD BE FIXED?

IF WE IMAGINED HE COULD *FIND* THE CAR, WE COULD PRETEND IT MIGHT BE FIXED.

I SEE.

YOU CAN KEEP THE BOOK. I'LL CALL THE BUS STATION.

"¿QUE PASA, SEÑORITA? ¡I AM EL FUGITIVO!"

IF YOU COULD WISH FOR ANYTHING, WHAT WOULD IT BE?

A BIG SUNNY FIELD TO BE IN.

A STUPID FIELD?! YOU'VE GOT THAT NOW! THINK BIG! RICHES! POWER! PRETEND YOU COULD HAVE ANYTHING!

WATTERSON

ACTUALLY, IT'S HARD TO ARGUE WITH SOMEONE WHO LOOKS SO HAPPY.

Z

HERE FISH!

THEY MUST KNOW THAT ONE.

WATTERSON

AAGHH!

CHOMP!

ARE THE FISH BITING?

DROP DEAD, HOBBES.

WATTERSON

I CAN'T GET THIS MODEL AIRPLANE TO LOOK RIGHT.

THESE DIRECTIONS ARE IMPOSSIBLE!

RRRRRGGGHHHHH

WHAM WHAM WHAM

HIT BY ANTI-AIRCRAFT GUNS.

YOUR PLANES DO SEEM TO RUN INTO THOSE, DON'T THEY?

TOMMY TOLD A FUNNY STORY AT SCHOOL TODAY. I ALMOST DIED!

TELL IT TO ME.

WELL, ACTUALLY THE STORY ITSELF WASN'T SO FUNNY...

...IT WAS THE *WAY* HE TOLD IT.

HOW DID HE TELL IT?

HE WAS DRINKING MILK AND WHEN HE LAUGHED, IT CAME UP HIS NOSE!

You've got two periods to live, Twinky.

Then it's gym class, and I turn you into hamburger casserole!

I HATE GYM CLASS.

COACH THINKS VIOLENCE IS AEROBIC.

 WHERE'S MY JACKET?

 I'VE LOOKED EVERYWHERE! UNDER THE BED, OVER MY CHAIR...

 ...ON THE STAIRS, ON THE HALL FLOOR, IN THE KITCHEN... IT'S JUST NOT ANYWHERE!

 OH, *HERE* IT IS! WHO PUT IT IN THE STUPID CLOSET?!?

 HOCUS-POCUS, ABRACADABRA!

 I COMMAND MY HOMEWORK TO DO ITSELF! **HOMEWORK, BE DONE!**

 FLIP FLIP FLIP

 RATS.

 DO YOU EVER THINK ABOUT THE END OF THE WORLD AS WE KNOW IT?

 YOU MEAN A NUCLEAR WAR?

 I THINK MOM WAS REFERRING TO IF SHE EVER CATCHES ME LETTING THE AIR OUT OF THE CAR TIRES AGAIN.

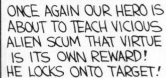

SO THE CONTRACTOR SAYS IT WILL COST ABOUT $200 TO FIX.

OH, THAT DUMB KID!

WELL, IT'S ALL PART OF RAISING A CHILD, RIGHT?

MM.

YOU'RE NOT SORRY WE HAD CALVIN, ARE YOU?

ARE *YOU*?

I ASKED FIRST.... BESIDES, IT WASN'T ALL *MY* DECISION.

ALL *I* KNOW IS THAT *I* OFFERED TO BUY US A DACHSHUND, BUT NO, *YOU* SAID...

DO YOU THINK THERE'S A GOD?

WELL *SOME*BODY'S OUT TO GET ME.

SPACEMAN SPIFF CLOSES IN ON THE ALIEN VESSEL!

THE ALIEN, BEING UNNATURALLY STUPID, IS BLISSFULLY IGNORANT OF ITS IMMINENT DOOM!

OUR HERO LOCKS ONTO TARGET AND WARMS UP HIS FRAP-RAY BLASTER!

MISS WORMWOOD!!

ZOUNDS! A GORKON DEATH STATION APPEARS! EVASIVE ACTION!

WHACK!

WOW! ANOTHER HOLE IN ONE!

WOW! THREE NEW MAGAZINES FOR ME TODAY.

YESTERDAY I GOT FIVE. I LOVE GETTING ALL THIS MAIL.

HOW COME YOU RECEIVE ALL THESE MAGAZINES?

I WENT TO THE LIBRARY AND FILLED OUT ALL THE SUBSCRIPTION CARDS THAT SAID "BILL ME LATER."

I LOVE SATURDAY MORNING CARTOONS.

WHAT CLASSIC HUMOR!

THIS IS WHAT ENTERTAINMENT IS ALL ABOUT.

... IDIOTS, EXPLOSIVES, AND FALLING ANVILS.

CALVIN, THE HUMAN INSECT, WALKS ACROSS THE DINNER TABLE.

WITH PROPORTIONAL INSECT STRENGTH, HE PLACES A GIANT PEA ON THE EDGE OF A SPOON.

HE THEN CLIMBS TO THE TOP OF THE OTHER END...

...AND WITH A TINY JUMP...

CALVIN, STOP THAT!

IN HIS MINUSCULE SIZE, IT TAKES CALVIN, THE HUMAN INSECT, TEN MINUTES TO WALK ACROSS A BOOK'S PAGE!

AT THE OTHER END, HE SLOWLY LIFTS THE GIGANTIC SHEET!

THEN IT'S ANOTHER TEN-MINUTE JOURNEY BACK, AS HE TURNS IT OVER!

GEE, THE KID'S BEEN QUIET FOR ALMOST TWENTY MINUTES.

HE'S DOING HIS HOMEWORK.

HERE'S A MOVIE WE SHOULD WATCH.

WHO'S IN IT?

IT SAYS, "JAPANESE CAST."

"TWO BIG RUBBERY MONSTERS SLUG IT OUT OVER MAJOR METROPOLITAN CENTERS IN A BATTLE FOR WORLD SUPREMACY."

DOESN'T THAT SOUND GREAT?

AND PEOPLE SAY THAT FOREIGN FILM IS INACCESSIBLE.

OH, ROSALYN, YOU'RE HERE! GOOD, COME IN!

WE REALLY APPRECIATE YOUR COMING ON SUCH SHORT NOTICE. WE'VE HAD A TERRIBLE TIME GETTING A BABY SITTER FOR TONIGHT.

HA HA, MAYBE LITTLE CALVIN HERE HAS GOTTEN HIMSELF A REPUTATION.

HA HA. YOU HAVE THE HALF UP FRONT?

YES, LET ME GET MY PURSE...

HI, BABY DOLL, IT'S ME. YEAH, I'M BABY SITTING THE KID DOWN THE STREET.

YEAH, THAT'S RIGHT, THE LITTLE MONSTER. ...HMM?... WELL SO FAR, NO PROBLEM.

HE HASN'T BEEN ANY TROUBLE. YOU JUST HAVE TO SHOW THESE KIDS WHO'S THE BOSS. ...MM HMM..

HOW MUCH LONGER TILL SHE LETS US OUT OF THE GARAGE?

SHE SAID 8 O'CLOCK, AND IT'S ALMOST 6:30 NOW...

THANKS AGAIN FOR BABY SITTING, ROSALYN.

CALVIN WAS NO TROUBLE AT ALL.

THAT'S GOOD. I'LL GET THE CAR AND DRIVE YOU HOME.

THERE YOU GO. GOOD NIGHT.

THANK YOU. GOOD NIGHT.

IS SHE GONE?

WHAT A GREAT NIGHT TO CAMP OUT!

WHERE'S OUR TENT? I THOUGHT THE SCOUTMASTER SAID TO SET THEM UP.

UH OH.

WHEN HE SAID TO PITCH THE TENT, I THREW IT AWAY.

THE BEST PART ABOUT THESE HIKES IS GETTING TO SEE SO MUCH WILDLIFE.

LOOK! A TIGER!

A TIGER?!

DON'T *DO* THAT!

WE'RE SEPARATED FROM THE TROOP AND HOPELESSLY LOST!

LEFT ALONE IN THE UNCOMPROMISING WILD TO SURVIVE BY OUR WITS UNAIDED!

HEY, DUMMY! THE SCOUTMASTER SAYS TO GRAB YOUR STUPID STUFFED TIGER AND GET YOUR REAR IN GEAR!

WE'LL TRY TO LOSE 'EM AGAIN OVER THE NEXT HILL.

GRAB THE HOTDOGS AND COME ON!

THE TROOP'S COOKING DINNER OVER THE FIRE.

OH THAT'S JUST GREAT.

HERE WE'VE BEEN LUGGING THIS DUMB MICROWAVE AROUND FOR NOTHING.

BOP

SPIKE!

OH OH, WE'D BETTER LEAVE!

IT LOOKS LIKE SOME BIG PEOPLE WANT TO PLAY TENNIS.

THE CROCODILE FLOATS TO THE TOP OF THE MURKY AMAZON...

COMPLETELY MOTIONLESS, HE APPEARS TO BE ONLY A HARMLESS LOG.

A HIPPOPOTAMUS APPROACHES AND ENSURES ITS INSTANT DEATH!

CALVIN, WHAT ARE YOU DOING? ARE YOU ALL RIGHT?

CLOSER... CLOSER...

MOM! MOM! A BIG DOG KNOCKED ME DOWN AND HE STOLE HOBBES!

I TRIED TO CATCH HIM, BUT I COULDN'T, AND NOW I'VE LOST MY BEST FRIEND!

WELL CALVIN, IF YOU WOULDN'T DRAG THAT TIGER EVERYWHERE, THINGS LIKE THIS WOULDN'T HAPPEN.

THERE'S NO PROBLEM SO AWFUL THAT YOU CAN'T ADD SOME GUILT TO IT AND MAKE IT EVEN WORSE!

I CAN'T SLEEP AT ALL. POOR HOBBES! I WONDER WHERE HE IS. I HOPE HE'S OK.

SNIFF.. WHAT DID I EVER DO TO DESERVE THIS?

WHATEVER IT WAS, I'M *SORRY* ALREADY!

LOST: MY TIGER, "HOBBES"

MAYBE YOU SHOULD DESCRIBE HIM.

ON THE QUIET SIDE. SOMEWHAT PECULIAR. A GOOD COMPANION, IN A WEIRD SORT OF WAY.

I MEAN, WHAT DOES HE LOOK LIKE?

OH.

WELL LOOK, SOMEBODY LEFT A STUFFED TIGER OUT IN THE FIELD. HOW STRANGE.

LOOKS LIKE A DOG'S BEEN CHEWING ON YOU, FELLA.

WELL, NOTHING A LITTLE TEA PARTY WITH SOME OTHER STUFFED ANIMALS WOULDN'T HELP. C'MON.

HOBBES! HOBBES! WHERE ARE YOU??

HELLO, CALVIN. WOULD YOU LIKE TO JOIN MY TEA PARTY?

HECK NO. I'M TRYING TO FIND MY BEST FRIEND, WHO'S BEEN KIDNAPPED BY A DOG. LEAVE ME ALONE.

WELL I THINK MR. CALVIN IS VERY RUDE, DON'T YOU, MR. TIGER? YES, I THINK SO TOO. MORE TEA, ANYONE?

HEY, I SHOULD TELL SUSIE TO KEEP HER EYES OPEN FOR HOBBES.

SUSIE, I... HOBBES!

YOU FOUND HOBBES! THANK YOU THANK YOU THANKYOUTHANKYOUTHANKY OUTHANKYOUTHANKYOUTHA

WELL! WASN'T MR. CALVIN A GENTLEMAN! I DO HOPE... HEY! WHO TOOK ALL THE COOKIES?!?

92

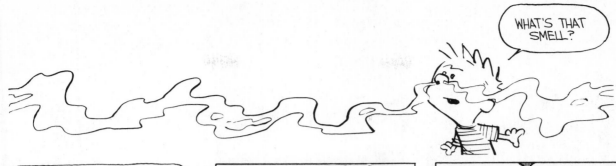

WHAT'S THAT SMELL?

EITHER MOM'S COOKING DINNER, OR SOMEBODY GOT SICK IN THE FURNACE DUCT.

BOY, DOES IT **STINK** IN HERE! WHAT ARE YOU COOKING FOR DINNER?!

WHATEVER IT IS, I'M NOT EATING IT.

I'M STEWING SOME MONKEY HEADS.

MONKEY HEADS?

THEY'LL BE SOGGY ENOUGH TO EAT IN ABOUT TWENTY MINUTES.

REALLY?? WE'RE HAVING MONKEY HEADS? WE ARE NOT. ...ARE THOSE REALLY MONKEY HEADS?

I'VE NEVER HAD MONKEY HEADS BEFORE! I WONDER WHAT THEY'RE LIKE.

WOW! MONKEY HEADS!

WATERSON

MM...KINDA SQUISHY. OOH LOOK, IS THAT A NOSE? WHAT'S THIS? BRAINS? I DIDN'T THINK THEY'D BE SO RUBBERY ...

WHAT? I THOUGHT THESE WERE STUFFED PEPPERS. HONEY, WHAT THE HECK **IS** THIS?? WHATEVER IT IS, I'M NOT EATING IT!

IT'S TOO EARLY TO BE IN BED. IT'S HARDLY EVEN DARK OUT. WHY DO I HAVE TO BE IN BED? IT'S RIDICULOUS.

I'M NOT EVEN TIRED! I DON'T NEED TO BE IN BED! THIS IS AN OUTRAGE!

IT'S THE STUPIDEST THING I CAN IMAGINE! I THINK MOM AND DAD ARE JUST TRYING TO GET RID OF ME. I CAN'T SLEEP AT ALL. CAN YOU SLEEP, HOBBES?

NO!

OK, MOM, HOBBES AND I HAVE FORMED A LOBBY. WE WANT MORE PRIVILEGES!

MORE PRIVILEGES? LIKE WHAT? YOU'VE GOT IT MADE!

NO RESPONSIBILITIES, NO CARES, NO WORRIES! WHAT MORE COULD YOU POSSIBLY WANT?

WHY DIDN'T YOU TELL HER ABOUT THE CREDIT CARDS IN OUR NAMES?

YOU HEARD HER. SHE'S IN ONE OF HER MOODS.

I LOVE SATURDAYS!

EVERY SATURDAY I GET UP AT SIX AND EAT THREE BOWLS OF CRUNCHY SUGAR BOMBS.

THEN I WATCH CARTOONS TILL NOON, AND I'M INCOHERENT AND HYPERACTIVE THE REST OF THE DAY.

DOES IT WORK?

NO BROTHERS OR SISTERS **SO** FAR!

THE WATER'S TOO COLD!

NOW IT'S TOO HOT.

NOW IT'S TOO COLD.

NOW IT'S TOO DEEP.

THE FEARSOME SHARK SENSES DISTRESS IN THE WAVES ABOVE HIM!

HE CIRCLES UP, CLOSER AND CLOSER TO THE TERRIFIED VICTIM!

HEY! YAHH! SNAP THRASH SNAP.

YOU KNOW, FOR SOMEONE WHO HATES BATHS AS MUCH AS YOU DO, YOU'RE NOT MAKING THIS GO ANY FASTER!

ANOTHER GRUESOME KILL...

I'VE NEVER BEEN THIS HIGH IN A TREE BEFORE.

ME EITHER. YOU CAN SEE FOR MILES FROM UP HERE.

I'LL SAY! I'M GLAD WE'RE UP HERE.

THAT WAS QUITE A CRASH, WASN'T IT?

THE RAIN STOPPED!

THIS IS THE BEST TIME TO GO WORMUCKING. LET'S GO!

WHAT'S THAT?

IT'S WHEN YOU WALK ON THE PAVEMENT AND MUCK ALL THE WORMS.

CALVIN, QUIT CHARGING AROUND THE HOUSE!!

SMASH!
BINK
BONK
BOOM

WHAT DID I JUST TELL YOU?!?

BEATS ME. WEREN'T YOU LISTENING EITHER?

EVERYBODY I KNOW HAS EITHER CABLE TV OR A VCR! THEY CAN WATCH ANYTHING THEY WANT!

BUT ME? *I* HAVE TO WATCH DUMB OL' SUMMER REPEATS! *I* HAVE TO WATCH THE SAME GARBAGE OVER AND OVER!

HOW CRUELLY WE MISTREAT YOU, CALVIN.

...SO THEN HE GAVE ME "OLIVER TWIST" TO READ, AND SAID I MIGHT IDENTIFY WITH IT.

RATS... AND "SORORITY ROW HORROR" IS ON CABLE TONIGHT.

I GOT A HELIUM BALLOON.

VERY NICE.

I'M GOING TO STAND ON THIS LADDER AND LET THE BALLOON CARRY ME UP AND AWAY.

NOTHING'S HAPPENING.

TRY JUMPING.

SEE? THERE GOES THE BALLOON. YOU DIDN'T HANG ON.

FLUSH!

WHEEE! HA HA HA!

I'M DONE WITH MY BATH.

MM... THAT WAS QUICK.

WHAT'S ALL THE RUCKUS?! YOU'RE SUPPOSED TO BE ASLEEP!

AND WHAT'S WITH ALL THESE FEATHERS?! ARE YOU TEARING UP YOUR PILLOWS?!

IT WAS INCREDIBLE, DAD! A HERD OF DUCKS FLEW IN THE WINDOW AND MOLTED! THEY LEFT WHEN THEY HEARD YOU COMING! HONEST!

NICE ALIBI, FRIZZLETOP! NO DESSERT FOR A WEEK!

YOU WANT ANOTHER PILLOW ACROSS THE KISSER? I DIDN'T HEAR *YOU* OFFER ANY BRAINSTORMS!

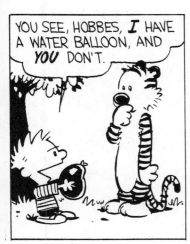

YOU SEE, HOBBES, *I* HAVE A WATER BALLOON, AND *YOU* DON'T.

I THEREFORE HAVE OFFENSIVE SUPERIORITY, SO YOU HAVE TO DO WHAT I SAY. WHAT DO YOU THINK OF THAT?

I THINK I'LL TAKE THIS STICK AND POKE YOUR BALLOON.

THAT'S THE TROUBLE WITH WEAPONS TECHNOLOGY. IT BECOMES OBSOLETE SO QUICKLY.

OH MY GOSH, HOBBES! **DON'T MOVE!**

WHAT? WHAT IS IT?

THE BIGGEST, UGLIEST, FUZZIEST CATERPILLAR I'VE EVER SEEN IS ABOUT TO CHOMP YOUR BOTTOM!

AAUGH! KILL IT! KILL IT!

YOW!

WHAM!

YOU KNOW WHAT **YOUR** PROBLEM IS? YOU'VE GOT NO APPRECIATION FOR PHYSICAL HUMOR, THAT'S WHAT!

WHEN ARE WE GOING TO GET TO OUR VACATION SITE? I WANNA *BE* THERE!

CALVIN, IT'S AN EIGHT-HOUR DRIVE. WE'RE NOT EVEN OUT OF OUR STATE YET. IT'S GOING TO BE A WHILE. RELAX.

HOW MUCH LONGER *NOW*?

I TOLD YOU WE SHOULD HAVE FLOWN.

THERE'S A RESTAURANT COMING UP. WANT TO STOP?

ONLY IF THEY HAVE HAMBURGERS.

HAMBURGERS? THAT'S ALL WE'VE EATEN THIS WHOLE STUPID TRIP! HAMBURGERS, HAMBURGERS, HAMBURGERS!

I'M SICK OF HAMBURGERS! WE'RE EATING SOMETHING ELSE FOR ONCE!

TEN MILLION BOTTLES OF BEER ON THE WALL, TEN MILLION BOTTLES OF BEER...

OK! OK! HERE'S A HAMBURGER JOINT! *ARE YOU HAPPY?!*

I HAVE TO GO TO THE BATHROOM.

CALVIN, WE JUST PULLED OUT OF THE RESTAURANT. CAN'T YOU WAIT? THINK OF SOMETHING ELSE.

ALL I CAN THINK OF IS NIAGARA FALLS, AND THE HOOVER DAM, AND NOAH'S ARK, AND...

OOH BOY, NOW *I* HAVE TO GO!

NEXT YEAR I SWEAR I'LL JUST TAKE A VACATION BY MYSELF.

THAT TRIP WAS EXCRUCIATING. THANK GOODNESS WE'RE HERE.

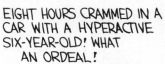

EIGHT HOURS CRAMMED IN A CAR WITH A HYPERACTIVE SIX-YEAR-OLD! WHAT AN ORDEAL!

WELL, NOW CALVIN CAN RUN AND SCREAM ALL HE LIKES. AHH, WHAT A GREAT LITTLE PLACE.

I'M BORED. WHEN ARE WE LEAVING?

YOU'RE BORED? WOULD YOU LIKE ME TO SHOW YOU HOW AN ANCHOR WORKS?

AHH! ANOTHER GLORIOUS SUNRISE, AND NOT A SOUL AROUND!

THIS IS THE LIFE! A BRISK SWIM AT DAWN, A MORNING OUT IN A BOAT...

...AND BY 9 A.M., I'M BACK WITH FRESHLY CAUGHT FISH FOR BREAKFAST! THE DAY'S HARDLY BEGUN! WHAT A VACATION!

UGH... I'VE SEEN CHEERIER FACES AT THE OFFICE!

YOU EAT YOUR DEAD ANIMALS. ALL I WANT IS SOME COFFEE.

WHY ISN'T THERE ANY TV UP HERE? I HATE THIS PLACE.

DAD, LOOK! I CAUGHT A FISH!

HEY, THAT'S A BIG ONE. I'LL SHOW YOU HOW TO CLEAN IT, AND WE'LL HAVE IT FOR DINNER.

"CLEAN IT"?

CUT OFF ITS HEAD AND GUT IT.

MMM! PASS ME ANOTHER OF THESE GREAT CHEESE SANDWICHES! HA HA, NO BONES IN THESE, RIGHT?

GUESS WHAT'S SHORT AND UGLY AND WET ALL OVER! ...GIVE UP?

THE ANSWER HAD BETTER NOT BE WHAT I THINK IT IS...

SQUIRT SQUIRT SQUIRT SQUIRT SQUIRT

YOW!

SQUIRT SQUIRT SQUIRT SQU

BANG BONK BING

CALVIN!

IF YOU'RE GOING TO TEAR AROUND, DO IT OUTSIDE!!

OKAY, OKAY...

IT'S ANOTHER NEW MORNING FOR MR. MONROE. HE GLANCES AT THE NEWSPAPER HEADLINES OVER A CUP OF COFFEE, AND GETS IN HIS RED SPORTS CAR TO GO TO WORK.

LITTLE DOES HE REALIZE IT'S HIS LAST DAY ON THE FACE OF THE EARTH!

CALVIN DRINKS THE MAGIC ELIXIR AND BEGINS AN INCREDIBLE TRANSFORMATION!

INSTANTLY HE GROWS! BIGGER AND BIGGER! HIGHER AND HIGHER!

HE IS NOW OVER 300 FEET TALL! THE FORMULA IS A SUCCESS!

CALVIN, THE MIGHTY GIANT, GOES ON A TERRIBLE RAMPAGE, STRIKING FEAR INTO THE HEARTS OF THE POPULACE!

NOTHING CAN STOP HIM! IT'S PANIC IN THE STREETS! A TOWN LIES IN RUINS!

NO, I WON'T BUY YOU ANY MORE TOY CARS. *I* SAW YOU! YOU DELIBERATELY STOMPED ON THOSE!

WATTERSON

C'MON, CALVIN! I SIGNED YOU UP FOR SWIMMING LESSONS.

I DON'T **WANT** SWIMMING LESSONS.!!

TOO LATE. LET'S GO.

WHAT ABOUT HOBBES? DID YOU SIGN HIM UP TOO?

NO, IT'S NOT GOOD TO GET TIGERS WET.

WHY IS *THAT*?

IT TAKES US ALL DAY TO DRY, AND UNTIL WE DO, WE SMELL FUNNY.

I CAN'T BELIEVE MY MOM SIGNED ME UP FOR SWIMMING LESSONS.

HERE I AM FREEZING MY BUNS OFF AT 9 IN THE MORNING, ABOUT TO JUMP INTO ICE WATER AND DROWN.

THE ONLY THING THAT COULD POSSIBLY MAKE THIS WORSE WOULD BE IF THE CLASS WAS...

...TAUGHT BY MY SADISTIC BABY SITTER!!

WELL, LOOK WHO'S HERE!

OK... EVERYONE IN THE WATER!

I REFUSE! I'M FREEZING ALREADY!

CALVIN, DO YOU KNOW WHAT A "RAT TAIL" IS?

NO.

IT'S WHEN YOU SOAK A TOWEL AND TWIST IT UP INTO A WHIP. IT STINGS LIKE CRAZY AND IS MUCH WORSE THAN BEING COLD. GET MY DRIFT?

I ALWAYS THOUGHT LIFEGUARDS WERE JUST TAUGHT HOW TO RESUSCITATE PEOPLE AND THINGS LIKE THAT.

HEY, MOM, ARE YOU NERVOUS?

NO. ...WHY?

CALVIN, GO OUTSIDE AND QUIT BUGGING ME!

CALVIN THE BUG BUZZES OFF!

FLYING LOW OVER THE GRASS, HE SEARCHES FOR DEAD MEAT!

UP AND OVER THE FLOWERS, DARTING THIS WAY AND THAT!

OH NO! HE'S CAUGHT IN A SPIDER WEB!

THRASHING ABOUT IN A DESPERATE BID FOR FREEDOM, HE ONLY BECOMES MORE ENTANGLED! SOON THE SPIDER WILL SUCK OUT HIS INNARDS! HELP!

WATTERSON

I WAS GOING TO JOIN YOU IN THE HAMMOCK, BUT I THINK I'LL FORGET IT.

HI, CALVIN, WHAT ARE YOU DOING?

BIG IMPORTANT SECRET THINGS! GO AWAY! GET LOST!

ALL RIGHT, DANDELION HEAD! WHO CARES WHAT YOU DO ANYWAY!

WE'RE DOING GREAT THINGS. WE'RE HAVING FUN!

I THOUGHT WE WERE BORED OUT OF OUR SKULLS.

OH HUSH. YOU DON'T KNOW ANYTHING.

THAT STUPID CALVIN. HE'S SO MEAN.

ALL I TRY TO DO IS BE FRIENDS, AND HE TREATS ME LIKE I'M NOBODY.

WELL, WHO NEEDS JERKS LIKE HIM ANYWAY? I DON'T NEED HIM FOR A FRIEND. I CAN HAVE FUN BY MYSELF!

POOP.

SUSIE, HOBBES THOUGHT I WAS RUDE, SO I'M SORRY, AND YOU CAN COME PLAY WITH US IF YOU WANT.

THANKS, CALVIN. THAT'S REALLY NICE OF YOU.

OK, WE'LL PLAY HOUSE NOW. I'LL BE THE HIGH-POWERED EXECUTIVE WIFE, THE TIGER HERE CAN BE MY UNEMPLOYED, HOUSEKEEPING HUSBAND, AND YOU CAN BE OUR BRATTY AND BRAINLESS KID IN A DAY CARE CENTER.

THIS WAS YOUR IDEA, PEA BRAIN.

DON'T YOU TALK TO YOUR FATHER THAT WAY!

I'M OFF TO WALL STREET. DON'T WAIT UP.

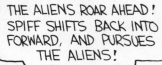
THE ALIENS ARE GAINING ON OUR HERO! IN A SURPRISE MOVE, SPACEMAN SPIFF SHIFTS INTO REVERSE!

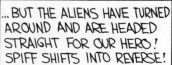
THE ALIENS ROAR AHEAD! SPIFF SHIFTS BACK INTO FORWARD, AND PURSUES THE ALIENS!

...BUT THE ALIENS HAVE TURNED AROUND AND ARE HEADED STRAIGHT FOR OUR HERO! SPIFF SHIFTS INTO REVERSE!

I'M GETTING SICK.

WHACK!

TELL ME THIS ISN'T A SPITBALL!!

HOBBES, QUICK! HOW DO I STOP?!?

STEER INTO A GRAVEL DRIVEWAY AND FALL DOWN!

SKRUNCH!

THAT WAS ONLY A SUGGESTION.

LOOK AT THAT THING IN THE DIRT! IT MUST BE A FOSSIL!

I WONDER WHAT PECULIAR ANIMAL *THIS* WAS.

BUT IT'S NOT A BONE. IT MUST BE SOME PRIMITIVE HUNTING WEAPON OR EATING UTENSIL FOR CAVE MEN.

MAYBE IT HAD SOME RELIGIOUS FUNCTION.

THIS EXPLAINS WHY YOUR CLOTHES STAY ON THE FLOOR.

MAKING A SIGN?

I'M DECLARING THE CREEK BACK IN THE WOODS "CALVIN'S CREEK."

WHEN YOU DISCOVER SOMETHING, YOU'RE ALLOWED TO NAME IT AND PUT UP A SIGN.

Calvins CrEEK

BUT SUPPOSE YOU DIDN'T DISCOVER THAT CREEK.

OF COURSE I DID! NOBODY *ELSE* HAS A SIGN THERE, RIGHT?

Hobs Crk

CAN HOBBES AND I GO PLAY IN THE RAIN, MOM?

NO.

WHY NOT?

YOU'LL GET SOAKED.

WHAT'S WRONG WITH THAT?

YOU COULD CATCH PNEUMONIA, RUN UP A TERRIBLE HOSPITAL BILL, LINGER A FEW MONTHS, AND DIE.

I ALWAYS FORGET. IF YOU ASK A MOM, YOU GET A WORST-CASE SCENARIO.

I HAD NO IDEA THESE LITTLE SHOWERS WERE SO *DANGEROUS.*

WANT TO GO SPELUNKING WITH ME?

SPELUNKING? THERE AREN'T ANY CAVES AROUND HERE!

YOU DON'T NEED A CAVE. ALL YOU NEED IS A ROCK.

SPELUNK!

WELL DAD, OFF TO WORK?

TOO BAD. *I'M* ON SUMMER VACATION, SO *I* GET TO STAY HOME AND DO WHATEVER I WANT.

WELL, GO OFF AND JOIN THE RAT RACE! MOM AND I ARE RACKING UP LOTS OF EXPENSES!

OOG.

I JUST DO THAT TO HELP HIM APPRECIATE THE WEEKENDS MORE.

HOT DAY, ISN'T IT?

I'LL SAY.

BUT IT'S THE HUMIDITY THAT REALLY GETS TO ME.

YOU DON'T LIKE IT WHEN IT'S HUMID?

NOT AT ALL.

THEN YOU'D BETTER GET OUT QUICK.

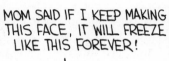

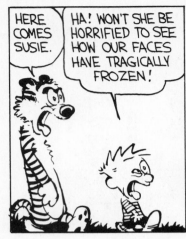

Panel 1: HERE COMES SUSIE. HA! WON'T SHE BE HORRIFIED TO SEE HOW OUR FACES HAVE TRAGICALLY FROZEN!

Panel 2: HI, SUSIE. HI, CALVIN.

Panel 3: WHAT DID YOU DO, GET YOUR HEAD STUCK IN THE BLENDER? IT'S AN IMPROVEMENT.

WATERSON

Panel 1: ARE THE COALS HOT?

Panel 2: YES, THEY'RE VERY HOT. I'M JUST ABOUT TO PUT ON THE HAMBURGERS.

Panel 3: BEFORE YOU DO, COULD YOU TOSS IN THE CAN OF LIGHTER FLUID AND MAKE A GIANT FIREBALL?

Panel 4: I'VE GOT THE MOST BORING DAD IN THE WORLD.

WATERSON

Panel 1: WITH THESE SNORKELS, WE CAN STAY UNDER WATER INDEFINITELY.

Panel 2: JUST THINK OF ALL THE FISH WE'LL BE ABLE TO SEE!

Panel 3: WE CAN COLLECT SHELLS! LET'S GO!

Panel 4: WELL SO FAR, THIS HAS BEEN A MAJOR DISAPPOINTMENT.

WATERSON

Finis